The Grouchy Dad

Written by Rebecca Ventre

Illustrated by Darya Shchegoleva

Today, my dad woke up on the wrong side of the bed!
From the moment he got up, HE was GROUCHY!

Dad promised to take me fishing today,
and even though I had to remind him 100 times,
HE was GROUCHY!

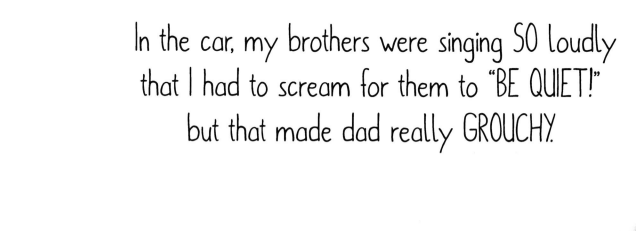

In the car, my brothers were singing SO loudly
that I had to scream for them to "BE QUIET!"
but that made dad really GROUCHY.

Dad asked me to help carry our fishing poles,
he must not have noticed that MY hands were full!

MY fishing hook got stuck,

and MY worm fell off,

and MY line got tangled,
but for some reason
HE was GROUCHY!

When we got home I tried to help him with the chores to cheer him up, but that made him
EVEN MORE GROUCHY!

I heard dad say to himself, "Don't lose your cool."
Maybe he needs help finding it!

At dinner, dad gave me the wrong color plate!
And even though MY dinner was ruined,
HE was GROUCHY!

Later that evening, dad said the big game was on,
but that didn't help his mood at all!

Dad asked me to clean my room,
but my legs were SO tired!

At bedtime, when dad came to tell me goodnight,
he stepped on one of my toys
which made him more GROUCHY than EVER!

Then, I remembered how dad helps me when I'm grouchy,
so I ran to get some supplies.
I handed him my favorite teddy bear and promised
it would stop hurting soon.
Dad smiled while I bandaged his foot.

I think he just needed a hug!

Made in United States
North Haven, CT
07 October 2023